clarinet

G000127427

THE BLUES BROTHERS

TAKE
THE
LEAD

clarinet

IMP

International
MUSIC
Publications

International Music Publications Limited
Griffin House 161 Hammersmith Road London W6 8BS England

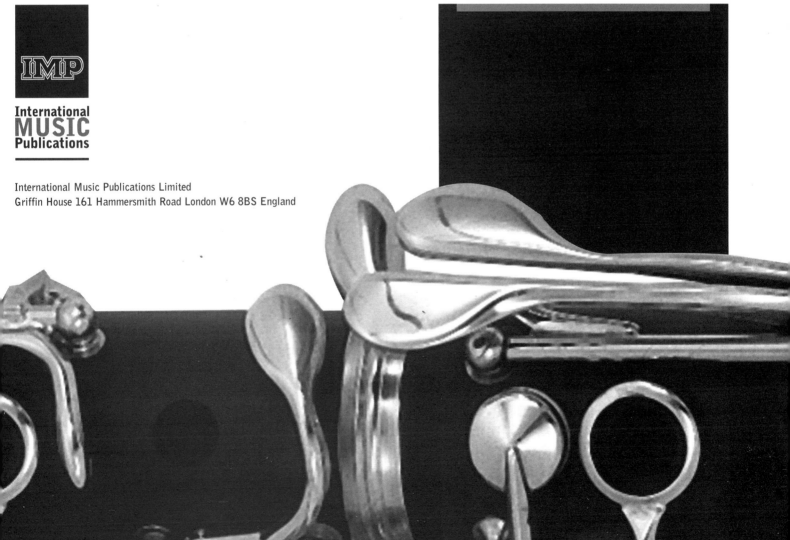

DON'T BE A MUSIC COPYCAT!

The copying of © copyright material is a criminal offence and may lead to prosecution.

Series Editor: Sadie Cook

Editorial, production and recording: Artemis Music Limited
Design and production: Space DPS Limited

Published 1999

International
MUSIC
Publications

International Music Publications Limited

England: Griffin House
161 Hammersmith Road
London W6 8BS

Germany: Marstallstr. 8
D-80539 München

Denmark: Danmusik
Vognmagergade 7
DK1120 Copenhagen K

Carisch

Italy: Via Campania 12
20098 San Giuliano Milanese
Milano

Spain: Magallanes 25
28015 Madrid

France: 20 Rue de la Ville-l'Eveque
75008 Paris

clarinet

TAKE THE LEAD

In the Book...

On the CD...

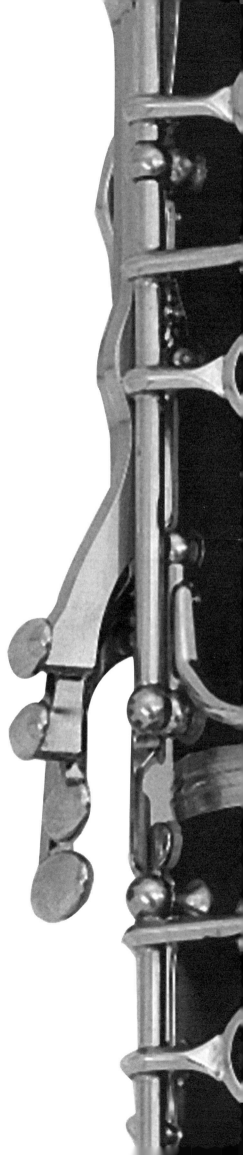

Demonstration   Backing

She Caught The Katy And
Left Me A Mule To Ride

Words and Music by
Taj Mahal and Yank Rachel

Demonstration   Backing

Gimme Some Lovin'

Words and Music by Steve Winwood,
Muff Winwood and Spencer Davis

Demonstration

Backing

Everybody Needs Somebody To Love

Words and Music by Bert Berns,
Solomon Burke and Jerry Wexler

Demonstration

Backing

Shake A Tail Feather

Words and Music by Otis Hayes,
Andre Williams and Verlie Rice

13

Demonstration

Backing

The Old Landmark

Words and Music by Adeline M Brunner

Demonstration   Backing

Think

Words and Music by
Ted White and Aretha Franklin

Minnie The Moocher

Words and Music by Cab Calloway,
Irving Mills and Clarence Gaskill

Demonstration   Backing

Sweet Home Chicago

Words and Music by Robert Johnson

10/99

Reproduced and printed by
Halstan & Co. Ltd., Amersham, Bucks., England

You can be the featured soloist with
TAKE THE LEAD

Now you can be the feature clarinet soloist on eight specially recorded arrangements

TAKE THE LEAD
clarinet

FEATURES
- Full backings to play along with
- Full demonstration tracks to help you learn the songs
- Carefully selected and edited arrangements
- Chord symbols in concert pitch

MOVIE HITS

Collect these titles, each with demonstration and full backing tracks on CD.

90s Hits	Movie Hits	TV Themes	Christmas Songs	The Blues Brothers
The Air That I Breathe (Simply Red)	**Because You Loved Me** (Up Close And Personal)	**Coronation Street**	**The Christmas Song (Chestnuts Roasting On An Open Fire)**	**She Caught The Katy And Left Me A Mule To Ride**
Angels (Robbie Williams)	**Blue Monday** (The Wedding Singer)	**I'll Be There For You (theme from Friends)**	**Frosty The Snowman**	**Gimme Some Lovin'**
How Do I Live (LeAnn Rimes)	**(Everything I Do) I Do It For You** (Robin Hood: Prince Of Thieves)	**Match Of The Day**	**Have Yourself A Merry Little Christmas**	**Shake A Tail Feather**
I Don't Want To Miss A Thing (Aerosmith)	**I Don't Want To Miss A Thing** (Armageddon)	**(Meet) The Flintstones**	**Little Donkey**	**Everybody Needs Somebody To Love**
I'll Be There For You (The Rembrandts)	**I Will Always Love You** (The Bodyguard)	**Men Behaving Badly**	**Rudolph The Red-Nosed Reindeer**	**The Old Landmark**
My Heart Will Go On (Celine Dion)	**Star Wars (Main Title)** (Star Wars)	**Peak Practice**	**Santa Claus Is Comin' To Town**	**Think**
Something About The Way You Look Tonight (Elton John)	**The Wind Beneath My Wings** (Beaches)	**The Simpsons**		**Minnie The Moocher**
Frozen (Madonna)	**You Can Leave Your Hat On** (The Full Monty)	**The X-Files**	**Sleigh Ride**	**Sweet Home Chicago**
			Winter Wonderland	
Order ref: 6725A – Flute	Order ref: 6908A – Flute	Order ref: 7003A – Flute	Order ref: 7022A – Flute	Order ref: 7079A - Flute
Order ref: 6726A – Clarinet	Order ref: 6909A – Clarinet	Order ref: 7004A – Clarinet	Order ref: 7023A – Clarinet	Order ref: 7080A - Clarinet
Order ref: 6727A – Alto Saxophone	Order ref: 6910A – Alto Saxophone	Order ref: 7005A – Alto Saxophone	Order ref: 7024A – Alto Saxophone	Order ref: 7081A - Alto Saxophone
Order ref: 6728A – Violin	Order ref: 6911A –Tenor Saxophone	Order ref: 7006A – Violin	Order ref: 7025A – Violin	Order ref: 7082A - Tenor Saxophon
	Order ref: 6912A – Violin		Order ref: 7026A – Piano	Order ref: 7083A - Trumpet
			Order ref: 7027A – Drums	Order ref: 7084A - Violin